Glencoe Science

Reading and Writing Skill Activities

Teacher Edition

Glencoe
McGraw-Hill

New York, New York   Columbus, Ohio   Woodland Hills, California   Peoria, Illinois

Glencoe Science

Student Edition
Teacher Wraparound Edition
Interactive Teacher Edition CD-ROM
Interactive Lesson Planner CD-ROM
Lesson Plans
Content Outline for Teaching
Dinah Zike's Teaching Science with Foldables
Directed Reading for Content Mastery
Foldables: Reading and Study Skills
Assessment
   Chapter Review
   Chapter Tests
   ExamView Pro Test Bank Software
   Assessment Transparencies
   Performance Assessment in the Science
     Classroom
   The Princeton Review Standardized Test
     Practice Booklet
Directed Reading for Content Mastery in Spanish
Spanish Resources
English/Spanish Guided Reading Audio Program

Reinforcement
Enrichment
Activity Worksheets
Section Focus Transparencies
Teaching Transparencies
Laboratory Activities
Science Inquiry Labs
Critical Thinking/Problem Solving
Reading and Writing Skill Activities
Mathematics Skill Activities
Cultural Diversity
Laboratory Management and Safety in the Science
   Classroom
MindJogger Videoquizzes and Teacher Guide
Interactive Explorations and Quizzes CD-ROM
Vocabulary Puzzlemaker Software
Cooperative Learning in the Science Classroom
Environmental Issues in the Science Classroom
Home and Community Involvement
Using the Internet in the Science Classroom

Glencoe/McGraw-Hill

A Division of The McGraw·Hill Companies

Send all inquiries to:
Glencoe/McGraw-Hill
8787 Orion Place
Columbus, OH 43240

ISBN 0-07-825448-5
Printed in the United States of America
6 7 8 9 10 009 06 05 04

Table of Contents

To the Teacher

This booklet is designed to help middle school students and teachers prepare for language arts proficiency tests. Activities allow students to practice language arts skills, while reinforcing science concepts. The activities correlate with Grade 6-8 content standards for the English language arts. The list of standards that appears on pages T5 and T6 was developed by the International Reading Association and the National Council of Teachers of English.

This book includes both reading and writing activities. Students are asked to consider purpose, form, and content in a wide variety of informational and real-world texts, including scientific articles, editorials, brochures, and Web pages. The activities require students to interpret, analyze, and create text, as well as identify correct language structure and conventions such as grammar, punctuation, and spelling. Each skill activity integrates one or more of the IRA/NCTE standards.

For a more detailed list of the standards and a discussion of their application, you may want to obtain a copy of Standards for the English Language Arts, A Project of International Reading Association & National Council of Teachers of English, 1996.
IRA Stock Number: 889
NCTE Stock Number: 46767-3050

How to Use This Book
The skill activities in this book have a dual purpose. Although the topics of the activities relate specifically to science, the exercises are designed to reinforce language arts skills.

The activities are referenced throughout the Teacher Wraparound Edition based on their science content. For example, an activity describing rain shadows is referenced in chapters that deal with climate. This allows you to use the activities to extend and enrich the chapter content, while at the same time helping students to prepare for language arts proficiency testing.

Before you assign activities, you may want to refer to the list of language arts standards that appears on pages T5 and T6 or obtain the extended version of standards from IRA/NCTE as listed above. The standards can help you customize your assignments based on the needs of individual students, groups of students, or the class as a whole.

Directions to students for using skill activities:
- Tell students to read the entire passage carefully before answering the questions.
- Recommend that they use context clues to try to understand words they don't recognize.
- Remind students that in writing activities they need to pay attention to grammar, punctuation, and spelling as well as content.
- Encourage them to develop their writing activities fully and in an organized manner.
- Let students know that in addition to understanding content, in many cases they will be asked to identify an author's point of view, the purpose of a piece or writing, or the audience to which it is targeted.

Standards for the English Language Arts

developed by the International Reading Association and the National Council of Teachers of English

1 *Students read a wide range of print and nonprint texts to build an understanding of texts, of themselves, and of the cultures of the United States and the world; to acquire new information; to respond to the needs and demands of society and the workplace; and for personal fulfillment. Among these texts are fiction and nonfiction, classic and contemporary works.*

2 *Students read a wide range of literature from many periods in many genres to build an understanding of the many dimensions (e.g., philosophical, ethical, aesthetic) of human experience.*

3 *Students apply a wide range of strategies to comprehend, interpret, evaluate, and appreciate texts. They draw on their prior experience, their interactions with other readers and writers, their knowledge of word meaning and of other texts, their word identification strategies, and their understanding of textual features (e.g., sound-letter correspondence, sentence structure, context, graphics).*

4 *Students adjust their use of spoken, written, and visual language (e.g., conventions, style, vocabulary) to communicate effectively with a variety of audiences and for different purposes.*

5 *Students employ a wide range of strategies as they write and use different writing process elements appropriately to communicate with different audiences for a variety of purposes.*

6 *Students apply knowledge of language structure, language conventions (e.g., spelling and punctuation), media techniques, figurative language, and genre to create, critique, and discuss print and nonprint texts.*

7 *Students conduct research on issues and interests by generating ideas and questions, and by posing problems. They gather, evaluate, and synthesize data from a variety of sources (e.g., print and nonprint texts, artifacts, people) to communicate their discoveries in ways that suit their purpose and audience.*

8 *Students use a variety of technological and informational resources (e.g., libraries, databases, computer networks, video) to gather and synthesize information and to create and communicate knowledge.*

9 *Students develop an understanding of and respect for diversity in language use, patterns, and dialects across cultures, ethnic groups, geographic regions, and social roles.*

10 *Students whose first language is not English make use of their first language to develop competency in the English language arts and to develop understanding of content across the curriculum.*

11 *Students participate as knowledgeable, reflective, creative, and critical members of a variety of literacy communities.*

12 *Students use spoken, written, and visual language to accomplish their own purposes (e.g., for learning, enjoyment, persuasion, and the exchange of information).*

For a more detailed list of the standards and a discussion of their application, you may want to obtain a copy of *Standards for the English Language Arts, A Project of International Reading Association & National Council of Teachers of English, 1996.*

IRA Stock Number: 889
NCTE Stock Number: 46767-3050

IRA/NCTE
Standard 1

Directions: *Read the magazine article below, then answer the questions.*

Cerro Grande Forest Fire Not What Was Prescribed

June 20, 2000—On May 5, a fire intentionally set by the National Park Service at Bandelier National Monument in New Mexico began burning out of control. What began as a prescribed burn became Cerro Grande fire—one of the worst fires in New Mexico's history. The fire was prescribed to remove brush and undergrowth in parts of the forest. By burning away this wildfire "fuel," the Park Service hoped to prevent a natural, uncontrollable wildfire from occurring. It also hoped to restore the natural cycle of fire necessary for forests to survive.

Forest fires can serve a purpose. The variety of plants in an area is often ten times greater after a wildfire because of the nutrient-rich soil that fires can produce. Fires burn mineral-storing parts of plants into ash. Rain or snow dissolves the ash into the soil, providing essential minerals to the soil. Some plants even depend on fire for survival. Many pine trees cannot reproduce without the help of fire. Their cones will not open and release seeds unless heated.

Many natural forest fires are started by lightning. However, it is common practice for the National Park Service to prescribe burns such as the one in New Mexico. Unfortunately in this case, good intentions had devastating results. Strong winds and hot weather caused the fire to spread rapidly, making it difficult to contain. By May 10, the fire had consumed more than 7,200 hectares of land. It also had destroyed many homes along the edge of the forest near Los Alamos, New Mexico. Thousands of people had to be evacuated. Embers from the fire were being carried up to a mile away by the wind, causing spot fires to erupt. When the fire was finally contained on June 6, it had burned almost 20,000 hectares of land, more than 200 homes, and caused more than $1 billion in damage.

Time will tell whether the forest will ultimately benefit from the fire or be forever damaged. The enormous amount of damage might outweigh any benefits. Most certainly, the lives of the people who watched the fire swallow up so much of the land have been forever changed.

Multiple Choice

1. What does the word *prescribed* mean in "prescribed burn"?
   a. to order
   b. to outlaw
   c. to give medical advice
   d. to claim a right to

2. Which is an opinion from the article?
   a. Many pine trees cannot reproduce without the help of fire.
   b. By June 6, the fire had consumed more than 20,000 hectares of land.
   c. Most certainly, the lives of the people who watched the fire swallow up so much of the land have been forever changed.
   d. Many natural forest fires are started by lightning.

3. What is a spot fire?
   a. a smaller fire burning in the middle of the main fire
   b. a fire set on the boundaries of a wildfire to control it
   c. a fire started away from the main wildfire by embers from it
   d. a fire intentionally set to control undergrowth and brush

Activity 1 (continued)

4. What caused the Cerro Grande fire to consume so much land so quickly?
   a. too much undergrowth
   b. spot fires erupting
   c. heavy rain
   d. strong winds

Short Answer

5. What is the author's attitude toward the National Park Service? Use information from the article to support your answer.

   _____

   _____

   _____

   _____

6. How would the article change if the author was writing it for a newspaper in Los Alamos, where many people lost their homes?

   _____

   _____

   _____

   _____

Activity 2

IRA/NCTE
Standard 1

Directions: *Read the passage below and examine the diagram. Then answer the questions.*

A rain shadow is an area that receives little rainfall because it is on the down-wind side of a mountain or mountain range. When winds encounter a mountain, air is forced to go up and over the mountain. As the air rises, it expands and cools. Cool air is unable to hold as much moisture as warm air, so the moisture often condenses, forming clouds. Precipitation then falls from the clouds on the upwind side of the mountain.

As air moves over the mountains and begins to descend on the downwind side, it becomes warmer. Clouds do not form easily in the warmer air. Because the warm, dry winds on the downwind side of the mountains produce very little precipitation, this area is called the rain shadow. In some parts of the world, rain shadow areas have become deserts because they receive so little rainfall. California's Death Valley is part of a rain shadow.

The following diagram illustrates how a rain shadow occurs.

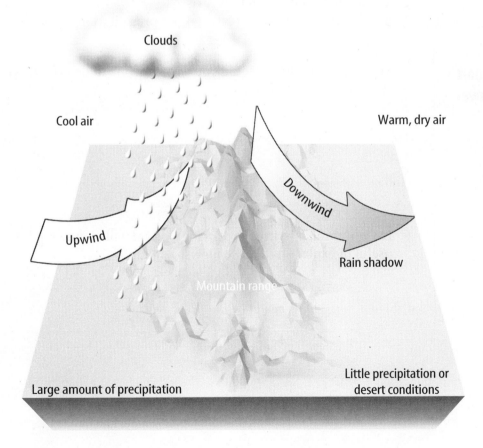

Clouds

Cool air

Warm, dry air

Downwind

Upwind

Rain shadow

Mountain range

Large amount of precipitation

Little precipitation or desert conditions

Activity 2 (continued)

Multiple Choice

1. What causes clouds to form on the upwind side of mountain ranges?
   a. The warm winds cause moisture to condense, forming clouds.
   b. The mountains keep the air from circulating, forming clouds.
   c. The strong winds push the air into the mountains, forming clouds.
   d. The air rises and cools as it hits the mountain, forming clouds.

2. Land in a rain shadow area most likely would
   a. be covered with thick forests.
   b. be desert.
   c. have many lakes.
   d. be used for farming.

3. Why did the author write this passage?
   a. to discuss how clouds form
   b. to tell how deserts are formed
   c. to give information about rain shadows
   d. to explain how mountains affect weather

4. Which detail is NOT supported in the passage?
   a. Some rain shadows are deserts.
   b. Death Valley is in California.
   c. Air cools and expands as it rises.
   d. The downwind side receives more precipitation.

Short Answer

5. What three questions could you ask someone to determine whether they live in a rain shadow?

   _____

   _____

   _____

   _____

6. Do you think a written explanation or a detailed drawing is most useful in explaining rain shadows? Explain.

   _____

   _____

   _____

Activity 3

IRA/NCTE
Standard 1

Directions: *Read the passage below, then complete the writing activity that follows.*

Keiko the killer whale, was the star of the *Free Willy* movies released in the 1990s. In 1996, it was revealed that Keiko was living in a cramped tank of warm water at an amusement park in Mexico. He was very sick. He captured the hearts of thousands of young people and environmentalists, who banded together to help him regain his freedom. He was moved to the Oregon Coast Aquarium to be rehabilitated. Once healthy, he was moved to an open-water pen in Klettsvik Bay off southern Iceland in 1998. The goal was to release him as soon as he was prepared to return to the wild. His crew of caretakers took him on several ocean "walks" to get him ready for his return to the sea.

When Keiko was finally granted his freedom, he refused to swim away. When his caretakers escorted him to the open seas, Keiko always returned. Because he has depended on humans for 20 years, Keiko had trouble readjusting to life in the wild. Hallur Hallsson, a spokesperson for the organization that cares for Keiko said, "It is likely that he will remain in captivity until the end of his life."

What is your reaction to Keiko's plight? Do you think people were justified in helping him win his freedom? Do you think they were disappointed when they learned he did not want to return to the wild? Write three personal journal entries that might have been written by someone who was involved in the "Free Willy" campaign.

1. The first entry should be written on the day that person decided to join the campaign.

2. The second entry should be written after Keiko's successful relocation to Iceland.

3. The third should be written after it was announced that Keiko showed no desire to return to the wild.

_____

_____

_____

_____

_____

_____

_____

_____

_____

_____

_____

Activity 3 (continued)

Directions: *Read the two newspaper articles below, then answer the questions.*

Navy Sonar May Be Responsible for Beached Whales

March 16— In the past two days, at least 16 whales have beached themselves on the shores of three islands in the Bahamas. Concerned bystanders were able to push some of the 12-foot to 15-foot whales back into the water, but seven of the whales have died.

Although the cause has not been determined, some scientists think that tests being conducted by the U.S. Navy in the area might be the cause of the whale's strange behavior. The ships were using sonar to detect submarines. Whales are highly sensitive to sound, and very loud noises created by the sonar tests could have disoriented the whales and even caused ear damage. Scientists said they will investigate to find the cause of the strange behavior. They plan to conduct necropsies on some of the whales to determine the cause of their deaths.

Report Released on Dead Whales

June 14— Marine biologists reported today that the seven whales who died last March in the Bahamas probably were disoriented by a "distant explosion or an intense acoustic event." The loud noise caused bleeding and damage to the tissues around the whales' inner ears, disorienting them and causing them to swim ashore.

Biologist Darlene Ketten of the National Marine Fisheries Service said that there might be a link between the death of the whales and the sound generated by Navy sonar tests, but she cannot say for sure. One possibility is that the loud noise was caused by an underwater landslide in the area.

According to the report, except for damage to their ears, the whales were healthy and free from disease. Whatever the cause, a Navy spokesperson said, "We hope to build upon what we will learn . . . to ensure that it does not happen again anywhere in the world."

Multiple Choice

1. What newsworthy event was the reporter writing about in these two articles?
   a. Seven whales died mysteriously.
   b. The Navy was conducting sonar testing.
   c. Research shows that whales are sensitive to sound.
   d. Scientists are performing tests on dead whales.

2. Most readers might infer from the first article that
   a. the whales died of natural causes.
   b. Navy sonar tests were probably responsible for the whales' deaths.
   c. these whales are on the endangered species list.
   d. the Navy is not responsible for the death of the whales.

3. In the last sentence of the first article, what does the word *necropsies* mean?
   a. written reports provided to government agencies
   b. medical examinations to determine cause of death
   c. X rays of vital organs
   d. underwater studies conducted on marine animals and plants

Activity 4 (continued)

4. Which of the following statements is NOT presented as a fact in either article?
   a. Navy sonar tests caused the death of the whales.
   b. Seven whales died in the Bahamas.
   c. Whales are sensitive to sound.
   d. Some of the whales examined had damage to their inner ears.

Short Answer

5. Do you think the Navy tests were responsible for the whales' deaths? Use information from the two articles to support your opinion.

   ....

   ....

   ....

   ....

6. What might be different about these two articles if the reporter was writing them for a team of marine biologists?

   ....

   ....

   ....

   ....

Activity 5

IRA/NCTE
Standard 2

Directions: *Read the passage below, then complete the writing activity that follows.*

One hundred years ago, no one would have expected that televisions, video cameras, compact disc players, and computers would be common household items. In the last century, technology has continually changed the way people do things. Sometimes technology makes life easier, and sometimes it makes it more difficult. Write an essay explaining how technology has affected your life. Discuss whether the effects have been positive or negative. Include specific details and examples from your life.

Activity 5 (continued)

_____
_____
_____
_____
_____
_____
_____
_____
_____
_____
_____
_____
_____
_____
_____
_____
_____
_____
_____
_____
_____
_____
_____
_____
_____
_____
_____
_____
_____
_____

Activity 6

IRA/NCTE
Standard 3

Directions: *Read the passage below, then answer the questions.*

The U. S. space program got a boost in 1997 with the Mars Pathfinder mission. Thousands of people watched as the Sojourner rover landed on Mars. The tiny rover, just 11 kg in weight and 0.6 m in length, could be controlled remotely from Earth. The goal of the mission was to study the environment of Mars. The rover gathered data on soil and rocks on the surface of Mars. It sent back incredible pictures of the Martian surface.

The Mars Pathfinder mission is part of NASA's Discovery missions—low-cost missions to explore Mars. But just how low is the cost? The Mars Surveyor '98 space program cost $193.1 million to develop, another $91.7 million to launch, and $42.8 million to run. This is a hefty price tag for a mission that failed.

The Mars Surveyor '98 was made up of two spacecraft—the *Mars Climate Orbiter* and the *Mars Polar Lander*. The Climate Orbiter reached Mars in September 23, 1999. It was scheduled to pass behind Mars and then reestablish radio contact with Earth. But no radio signal was ever received. Scientists think a mix-up of English and metric measurements caused the Orbiter to get too close to Mars and burn up in its atmosphere.

The *Mars Polar Lander* encountered a similar fate just months later when it disappeared on December 3, 1999. Its mission was to search for water and ice at Mars' south pole. But communication was lost and it's not known whether it ever landed on the planet. A report on the mission assumes that the Lander crashed into the surface of Mars. Apparently, the legs of the Lander interfered with communications. This led scientists to believe that it had landed, so they turned off the engines, making it impossible for it to land safely.

The two lost spacecraft were valued at $320 million. It's time to reexamine our goals in space exploration and determine whether or not it's worth the price. We cannot continue to invest dollars in space programs and receive nothing in return.

Multiple Choice

1. Which two spacecraft on the Mars Surveyor '98 were lost?
   a. *Polar Lander* and *Climate Orbiter*
   b. *Climate Orbiter* and *Sojourner*
   c. *Pathfinder* and *Polar Lander*
   d. *Climate Orbiter* and *Pathfinder*

2. What was NASA's first clue that the *Climate Orbiter* might be in trouble?
   a. It did not reestablish radio contact after passing behind Mars.
   b. It was orbiting too close to Mars.
   c. The engines were turned off.
   d. The rover sent back pictures of the mishap.

3. Where would an article like the one you just read most likely be published?
   a. in an encyclopedia
   b. on the editorial page of a newspaper
   c. in a factual report written by NASA engineers
   d. in a letter to members of Congress to gather support for the space program

Activity 6 (continued)

4. Which of these statements from the article is NOT an opinion?
    a. It's time to reexamine our goals in space exploration and determine whether or not it's worth the price.
    b. We cannot continue to invest dollars in space programs and receive nothing in return.
    c. The two lost spacecraft were valued at $320 million.
    d. This is a hefty price tag for a mission that failed.

Short Answer

5. In the last sentence, the author writes, "We cannot continue to invest dollars in space programs and receive nothing in return." Do you agree with this statement? Explain.

6. How do you think a group of NASA engineers who worked on this mission might respond to this article?

IRA/NCTE
Standard 3

Directions: *Examine the map and read the weather report. Then answer the questions.*

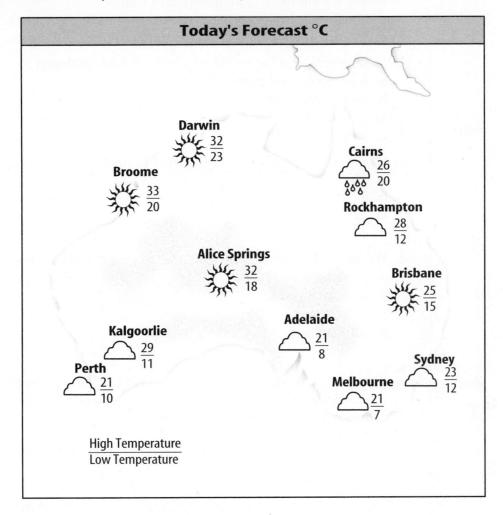

Today's Forecast °C

Darwin $\frac{32}{23}$

Cairns $\frac{26}{20}$

Broome $\frac{33}{20}$

Rockhampton $\frac{28}{12}$

Alice Springs $\frac{32}{18}$

Brisbane $\frac{25}{15}$

Adelaide $\frac{21}{8}$

Kalgoorlie $\frac{29}{11}$

Perth $\frac{21}{10}$

Sydney $\frac{23}{12}$

Melbourne $\frac{21}{7}$

$\frac{\text{High Temperature}}{\text{Low Temperature}}$

The forecast for today calls for fairly warm temperatures around much of Australia. The temperatures will stay in the low 30s for much of northwest Australia. Those areas also can expect continued sun. Clouds cover much of the rest of the country with the Sun peaking through only occasionally. You'll want to carry an umbrella in Cairns and a light jacket along much of the southern coast, as the low temperatures will dip into the 30s. All in all, expect a beautiful spring day and much of the same throughout the rest of the week.

Activity 7 (continued)

Multiple Choice

1. If the map is correct, what is the one incorrect fact in the weather report?
   a. Northwest Australia will have temperatures in the 30s.
   b. You'll want to carry an umbrella in Cairns.
   c. You'll want to carry a light jacket along much of the southern coast.
   d. Overnight temperatures on the southern coast will dip into the 30s.

2. Most people who live in Alice Springs probably will wear
   a. long sleeves and pants.
   b. shorts and a tank top.
   c. a sweatshirt and shorts.
   d. long pants and a T-shirt.

3. What is the expected low temperature in Adelaide?
   a. 21
   b. 8
   c. 12
   d. 23

4. You most likely would find a weather map with today's forecast in
   a. an almanac.
   b. an encyclopedia.
   c. a newspaper.
   d. a magazine.

Short Answer

5. This weather report was written to inform but it is written in a friendly, informal tone. Give an example of one or two words or phrases that help to make the report reader-friendly.

   _____

   _____

6. The weather report states, "all in all, expect a beautiful spring day." Write at least one detail from the passage that does NOT support this idea.

   _____

   _____

IRA/NCTE
Standard 4

Directions: *Read the article below, then answer the questions.*

On the Edge of Extinction

In 1900, there were an estimated 100,000 tigers on Earth. Today, only between 5,000 and 7,500 remain. Total extinction of tigers by 2010 is a very real threat.

Why are tigers disappearing? The criminal act of poaching is the main reason. Poaching is illegal, but it is very profitable. Tiger parts are worth large amounts of money. The parts of a single tiger can be worth $5 million. In the past, the hide of the tiger was a great prize; now the prize is the tiger's bones. The bones are used to make many traditional Asian medicines. Many of these medicines are exported from Asia, some of them to the United States. In 1950, about 4,000 South China tigers lived in the wild. By 1998, this number had dropped to less than 30 wild tigers.

Even though the U. S. Congress passed legislation to stop the import of tiger parts, poachers continue to get around the rules. They smuggle tiger parts in with other legal products. The United States has fewer than 100 wildlife inspectors to check products coming into the country. It is not difficult to get tiger parts into the country without being caught. Even when inspectors find medicines made with tiger bones, they cannot always prove it. The high temperature needed to make the medicines makes it impossible to tell whether the bone was that of a tiger or another animal.

You would expect most tiger products to be sold in secret in the United States. Many of them are sold openly in small medicine shops in some of the nation's larger cities. The demand for the products is great enough to outweigh the risk of getting caught selling them.

Some groups are working to decrease the number of tiger products sold, by helping find other options. For example, the bones of wild mole rats, a species that is abundant, have been used to make medicines. Finding alternatives to create less demand for tiger parts is one of the first steps to ending tiger poaching.

Multiple Choice

1. The main idea of this article is that
   a. poaching tigers is illegal.
   b. tiger bones are used in medicine.
   c. more needs to be done to stop the poaching of tigers.
   d. poachers smuggle tiger parts into the United States.

2. This passage does NOT discuss
   a. where tiger medicines are sold in the United States.
   b. how tiger parts are exported from Asia.
   c. alternatives to using tiger bones in medicine.
   d. the number of tigers living in the wild.

3. Why did the author write this passage?
   a. to show people how to smuggle tiger parts
   b. to tell people where to find tiger medicines
   c. to inform people about tiger poaching
   d. to tell people which tiger part to use for laziness

Activity 8 (continued)

4. In the third paragraph, what is the meaning of the word *legislation*?
   a. plans
   b. ideas
   c. tests
   d. laws

Short Answer

5. If you wanted to persuade someone that tiger poaching is wrong, do you think a written, spoken, or visual message might be most effective? Why?

_____
_____
_____
_____
_____

6. What support does the author give for the statement, "Total extinction of tigers by 2010 is a very real threat"? Give two examples.

_____
_____
_____
_____
_____
_____
_____
_____

Activity 9

IRA/NCTE
Standard 4

Directions: _Read the passage below, then complete the writing activity that follows._

Your seven-year-old neighbor has just developed a new interest in science and wants to learn all that she can. You know that many examples of science are all around you, so you decide to take her on a science tour of your house or your neighborhood to point them out. Write a detailed description of a tour that you might plan for your young neighbor. Your tour should include at least five examples of everyday objects or events that illustrate common science concepts. Your examples could illustrate changes in states of matter; elements and their properties; simple machines, such as wheels and axles or levers; temperature and heat; action and reaction; gravity; or any other science concepts that you could explain easily to a seven-year-old. List your examples in the order in which you would visit them on your tour. Then write what you would say about each.

_____

_____

_____

_____

_____

_____

_____

_____

_____

_____

_____

_____

_____

_____

_____

_____

_____

_____

_____

_____

Activity 9 (continued)

Activity 10

IRA/NCTE
Standard 5

Directions: *Read the passage below, then answer the questions.*

Ice sheets are huge massess of ice that form in some places where snow falls faster than it can melt. The world's second largest ice sheet is the 1.8 million-square-km sheet of ice that covers most of Greenland. Gravity causes the ice to flow from higher elevations at the center of the ice sheet to lower elevations at the edges. In some places, the ice reaches the sea where it breaks off and forms icebergs.

Recently it has become possible to directly measure whether parts of the ice sheet are thickening or thinning. Researchers from NASA and other places used a laser mounted on an airplane to measure the height of the southern part of the ice sheet surface in 1993 and 1994, and again in 1998. Their results showed that while much of the ice sheet was thickening slowly, near the southeastern coast the ice sheet was thinning by as much as several meters per year.

The size of the measured thinning was suprising. One possible explanation is that the ice is thinning in response to a warming climate. Since the last part of the nineteenth century, Earth's mean temperature has increased by about 1°C. Measurements show that the 1990s were the warmest decade of the past 100 years, while 1998 was the warmest year since 1860. This increase in Earth's average temperature often is called global warming. Global warming may be causing part of the ice sheet to thin.

Some scientists suspect that global warming may be caused by an increase in greenhouse gases in Earth's atmosphere. Burning fossil fuels produces the greenhouse gas carbon dioxide. Measurements show that the amount of carbon dioxide in the atmosphere has been increasing since the middle of the eighteenth century. Global warming has been occurring over the time that carbon dioxide levels have been rising.

If global warming caused the Greenland ice sheet to completely melt, the result could be catastrophic. The ice sheet contains enough ice to raise the level of the ocean by about 6 m if it were completely melted. If this were to happen, coastal cities throughout the world, such as New York City, would experience massive flooding.

Multiple Choice

1. According to the passage, what might be causing part of the Greenland ice sheet to thin?
   a. too little snow
   b. global warming
   c. carbon dioxide
   d. rising sea levels

2. What is the definition of the word *mean* in the third paragraph?
   a. average
   b. lowest
   c. highest
   d. Fahrenheit

Activity 10 (continued)

3. What is the author's attitude about global warming?
 a. The author thinks it will not change Earth's climate.
 b. The author thinks it is only a theory.
 c. The author does not take it seriously.
 d. The author thinks it has occurred.

4. This passage suggests that what is happening in Greenland
 a. will cause the Greenland ice sheet to disappear.
 b. should not be a concern for scientists.
 c. might be due to global warming.
 d. will increase Earth's temperature.

Short Answer

5. How did researchers measure the thickening and thinning of the ice sheet?

6. Why do you think the author wrote this passage? If the last paragraph of the passage was deleted would your response be the same? Explain.

Activity 11

IRA/NCTE
Standard 5

Directions: *Read the travel brochure below, then answer the questions.*

Canyon Rock Tours
South Rim Drive
(555) 602-7548

"A unique look at the Grand Canyon from a geologist's perspective."
Let our professional geologists give you the most
informative Grand Canyon tour available.

The Rocks

Learn about the amazing history of the
Grand Canyon by looking at its many layers
of rock. See trace fossils of animals and
plants that lived millions of years ago. Touch
Precambrian rocks that are 2 billion years
old. Find out which minerals give the rock
layers their colors of red, yellow, and green.

The Formations

Visit different rock formations and witness
how erosion and weathering have shaped one
of the world's most beautiful canyons.

The Views

Enjoy your lunch break at Yavapai Observa-
tion Station. The station overlooks the
canyon with a view that is breathtaking and
unforgettable.

- Tours depart every day, except Sunday, at 9 A.M. from the Grand Canyon
  Village Visitor Center. Tours return around 5 P.M.
- Cost is $30 per person.
- Be sure to pack a sack lunch and bring plenty of drinking water.
- This tour involves extensive hiking and requires some rock-climbing
  experience. Please dress in layers and wear appropriate shoes.
Note: Reservations are required at least two days in advance for groups of six or more.

Multiple Choice

1. Which of the following statements from this brochure is a form of bias?
   a. Find out which minerals give the rock layers their colors of red, yel-
      low, and green.
   b. Let our professional geologists give you the most informative Grand
      Canyon tour available.
   c. Touch Precambrian rocks that are 2 billion years old.
   d. Cost is $30 per person.

2. Which shoes would be most appropriate for this tour?
   a. sneakers
   b. sandals
   c. dress shoes
   d. hiking boots

3. Tourists are required to make reservations at least two days in advance if
   a. they have a group of six or more people.
   b. they want to go on a certain day.
   c. they do not want to pack a lunch.
   d. they would like a private tour.

4. Who would be most likely to take this tour?
   a. people who want to see the Colorado River
   b. people who do not like to hike
   c. people who are interested in rocks
   d. people who want to hike across the Grand Canyon

Short Answer

5. Your 70-year-old grandfather, who uses a wheelchair, did not get a chance to see this brochure. He's interested in geology and thinks he'd like to go on the tour Sunday at 11 A.M. He's willing to spend up to $25. He asked you if the tour is a good choice for him. What do you tell him? Explain your answer using details from the brochure.

_____

_____

_____

_____

6. The brochure contains factual information and opinions. List one opinion from the brochure and explain what makes it an opinion.

_____

_____

_____

_____

Activity
12

IRA/NCTE
Standard 5

Directions: *Read the passage below, then complete the writing activity that follows.*

   Students in Pennsylvania are cleaning up—cleaning up waste, that is. School districts throughout the state have started recycling programs or have expanded existing ones. As a result of their efforts, waste disposal costs have decreased, students have learned more about environmental issues, and important natural resources have been saved.

   These students have worked hard to ensure that their recycling programs are successful. One of the things they did to get their programs off the ground was to concentrate on a single area of the school that is a source of a lot of recyclables. For example, some programs focused on recycling soft-drink cans and other materials from the school cafeteria. Other programs recycled newspapers, magazines, and paper from the school library. Students set up collection bins throughout the school and made sure the other students knew about them. The bins were clearly marked so recycling became an easy, everyday habit for students and staff. Students also involved school custodians and partnered with a local recycling service company to pick up the materials in the bins. Finally, students used the school newspaper, the school Web site, and handcrafted posters to educate and reeducate students and staff about the benefits of recycling.

   According to the Pennsylvania Department of Environmental Protection, recycling paper cuts air pollution by 75 percent. Recycling a ton of glass saves the equivalent of 34 L of fuel oil. Recycling just one soft-drink can save enough electricity to light a 100-W bulb for 3.5 hours.

Write a persuasive letter to your school principal suggesting a school recycling program. Be sure to include reasons why recycling is a good idea, details on how the program should work, and how you plan to promote the project. Remember to write in formal letter format.

_____

_____

_____

_____

_____

_____

_____

_____

_____

_____

_____

Activity 12 (continued)

Activity 13

IRA/NCTE
Standard 6

Directions: *Read the passage below, then answer the questions.*

In the United States, 33 million people become sick each year from food-borne illnesses and 5,000 to 9,000 people die. One way to make foods safer is to expose them to radiation. This process, called irradiation, kills harmful bacteria and parasites and slows spoilage. Some people do not approve of the use of irradiation. They say its safety has not been proved. Those who support its use say it will make safe food available to more people. The World Health Organization, an agency that sets global standards for health, supports irradiation as a way of protecting the public's health.

Multiple Choice

1. Which of the following sentences would be the best topic sentence for this paragraph?
   a. Radiation is energy that travels by waves in all directions from its source.
   b. Food poisoning is a real problem.
   c. In 1930, a French scientist patented a process of irradiation.
   d. The bacterium that causes botulism is *clostridium botulinum.*

2. Which of the following sentences contains a misspelled word?
   a. One way to make foods safer is to expose them to radiation.
   b. They say its safety has not been proved.
   c. The World Health Organization, an agency that sets global standards for health, supports irradiation as a way of protecting the public's health.
   d. Those who support its use say it will make safe food availible to more people.

3. What is the subject of the sentence: The World Health Organization, an agency that sets global standards for health, supports irradiation as a way of protecting the public's health.
   a. The World Health Organization
   b. agency
   c. health
   d. irradiation

4. If you divided this paragraph into two paragraphs, which sentence would you choose to be the first sentence of your second paragraph?
   a. Some people do not approve of the use of irradiation.
   b. They say its safety has not been proved.
   c. This process, called irradiation, kills harmful bacteria and parasites and slows spoilage.
   d. One way to make foods safer is to expose them to radiation.

Activity 13 (continued)

**Short
Answer**

5. Create two simple sentences from one of the compound sentences in the passage.

   _____

   _____

   _____

   _____

6. If you wanted to develop this paragraph into a more complete article, list three topics you would develop further.

   _____

   _____

   _____

   _____

   _____

   _____

IRA/NCTE
Standard 6

Directions: *Read the passage below, then complete the writing activity that follows.*

Montserrat is a small island in the Caribbean that is governed by Britain. In 1995, Montserrat's Soufriére Hills volcano became active. It erupted in September 1996 and again on June 25, August 3, September 21, and December 26, 1997. It caused extensive damage on the island. Nineteen people were killed in one of the 1997 explosions. Almost 7,000 of the island's 11,000 residents permanently left the island. Dozens of islanders stayed, however, saying they did not want to move to overcrowded and unsanitary shelters.

In 1998, the volcano became silent. Scientists and islanders thought things were back to normal. Islanders looked forward to moving back. But in November 1999, the volcano began spewing molten rock. In March 2000, the volcano briefly exploded—proving it was not going to remain silent.

Imagine you are a resident and have chosen not to leave the island. Write a narrative describing what you will do if the volcano erupts again.

_____

_____

_____

_____

_____

_____

_____

_____

_____

_____

_____

_____

_____

_____

_____

_____

_____

Activity 14 (continued)

IRA/NCTE
Standard 7

Directions: *Read the passage below, then answer the questions.*

Chesapeake Bay is the largest estuary in the United States. An estuary is a body of water along a coast in which river and seawater mix. More than 100,000 streams and rivers drain into the Chesapeake Bay from Delaware, Maryland, New York, Pennsylvania, Virginia, West Virginia, and the District of Columbia. Its watershed, or drainage basin, covers 26 hectares. More than 15 million people live in the watershed. This huge population has had a great impact on the bay and its plants and animals.

Everything that happens in the watershed affects the bay. The same rivers and streams that drain into the bay also add pollutants. Some pollutants take a very indirect route. For example, a farmer might spray a pesticide on his field. A thunderstorm then could wash some of that pesticide into a creek. The creek could flow into a river and the river into the bay, carrying the pesticide pollutants with it.

Pollutants also can take a direct route to the bay. Many wastewater treatment plants release effluent into the bay. Effluent is water with waste material in it. Effluent contains an excess of two nutrients—nitrogen and phosphorus. Although these nutrients are necessary for life, they can be very harmful to the bay. They cause algae in the water to grow out of control. This sudden explosion of algae is called an algal bloom. Algal blooms block the sun and cause underwater plants to die. This has a ripple effect on the animals in the estuary that depend on the underwater plants for food. When the algae dies and begins to decompose, it also uses up precious oxygen supplies, causing fish and other living things to die.

The good news for the bay is that people are trying to save it. In 1983, the states in the watershed, as well as the Environmental Protection Agency, signed an agreement to protect the bay. They signed a similar agreement in 1987 and again in 2000. As part of the agreement, effluent entering Chesapeake Bay is treated before it's released. This is one way of reducing the amount of nitrogen and phosphorus that enters the bay. More people also are becoming aware of how their actions directly affect the bay. Cleanup efforts and environmental awareness are having a positive effect on the bay.

Multiple Choice

1. The best synonym for the term *effluent* is
   a. algal bloom.
   b. watershed.
   c. waste material.
   d. estuary.

2. What is the main cause of algal blooms?
   a. untreated wastewater
   b. excess nitrogen and phosphorus
   c. runoff water from thunderstorms
   d. too little oxygen in the water

Activity 15 (continued)

3. When was the first Chesapeake Bay agreement signed?
   a. 1983
   b. 1987
   c. 1993
   d. 2000

4. Which of the following is not directly stated in the passage but can be inferred?
   a. People should think about how things they do affect the bay.
   b. Wastewater treatment plants should pay to clean up the bay.
   c. Farmers are causing the most pollution in the bay.
   d. Pesticides should not be used by states that border the bay.

Short Answer

5. Give an example of how a pollutant from 300 km away might get into Chesapeake Bay.

   _____

   _____

   _____

   _____

   _____

6. Name one thing that people living in the Chesapeake Bay watershed can do to help protect the bay.

   _____

   _____

   _____

   _____

   _____

Activity
16

IRA/NCTE
Standard 7

Directions: *Read the passage, then complete the writing activity that follows.*

Every year, the United States government funds research on many different diseases. This research has led to better treatments, vaccines, and even cures. In 1999, the National Institutes of Health had an annual budget of $15.6 billion. That amount was one-fourth the total spent publicly and privately worldwide on disease research. Much of the money was spent on research for diseases such as AIDS, breast cancer, and diabetes. Diseases that affect a greater number of people usually receive more funding for research.

On which disease do you think the government should spend the most research money? Why? Write a statement to express your opinion. Include information to support your belief and list at least three reasons to defend your position. You might want to include whether or not you or someone you know has been affected by the disease.

_____
_____
_____
_____
_____
_____
_____
_____
_____
_____
_____
_____
_____
_____
_____
_____
_____
_____

Activity 16 (continued)

Activity 17

IRA/NCTE

Standard 8

Directions: *Read the passage below, then complete the writing activity that follows.*

Microwave ovens are convenient because they cook food so quickly. Today, they are commonplace and inexpensive. However, in 1952, when they first came on the market, the few people who could afford to buy them had to pay more than a thousand dollars.

Microwaves are very efficient. They use little electricity because they heat only the food. The oven generates high-frequency electromagnetic waves, called microwaves. The water, fats, and sugars in the food absorb these microwaves. Then the molecules in the food begin to move or become "excited." All of this movement generates heat inside the food. That's why microwaves cook food from the inside out.

Most plastics and glassware do not absorb microwaves. That's why they are used in microwave cooking. Metal, on the other hand, blocks microwaves. That's why foods cannot be microwaved in metal containers. Even a small piece of aluminum foil can make sparks fly inside a microwave.

Based on your own experience, compose a set of step-by-step instructions explaining how to use a microwave oven. Be sure to include a short list of do's and don'ts. If you do not have a microwave or have never used one, choose another household appliance on which to base your instructions.

_____

_____

_____

_____

_____

_____

_____

_____

_____

_____

_____

_____

_____

_____

_____

Activity 17 (continued)

Activity

18

IRA/NCTE
Standard 8

Directions: *Examine the diagram and read the description that follows. Then answer the questions.*

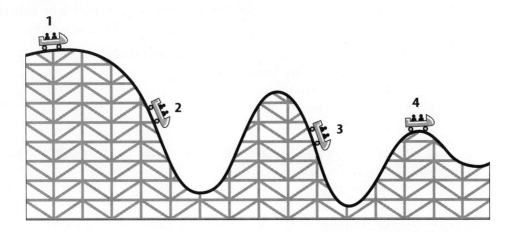

Roller coasters are among the most popular amusement park rides. They are exhilarating and thrilling to the people who ride them. How a roller coaster works is quite simple.

1. Almost all roller coasters start by going up a hill. The coaster is pulled up the hill by a moving chain. A motor provides the energy for the moving chain. The energy from the motor is transferred to the coaster.

2. At the top of the hill, the coaster has stored energy. It has the most stored energy on the first hill. As the coaster goes over the top of the hill, the chain is released and the coaster falls freely on the tracks.

3. As the coaster moves rapidly down the first hill, its stored energy changes into energy of motion, or kinetic energy. It has kinetic energy because it is moving. This kinetic energy carries it to the top of the next hill.

4. The kinetic energy is converted back into stored energy when the coaster reaches the top of the second hill. As it goes down the second hill, the stored energy is again changed into kinetic energy. This happens over and over on each hill until the coaster reaches the station and is stopped by the coaster's operator.

   Note: Each hill of a roller coaster must be smaller than the one before it for the coaster to have enough energy to make it over all of the hills. The coaster loses some of its energy between hills because of track friction and air resistance.

Multiple Choice

1. Which number on the diagram shows the roller coaster at the point where it has the most stored energy?
   a. 1
   b. 2
   c. 3
   d. 4

Activity 18 (continued)

Multiple Choice

2. Which statement from the passage is an opinion?
 a. A motor provides the energy for the moving chain.
 b. Almost all roller coasters start by going up a hill.
 c. They are exhilarating and thrilling to the people who ride them.
 d. The energy from the motor is transferred to the coaster.

3. Where would you be most likely to find this passage?
 a. in a chemistry book
 b. in an almanac
 c. in a physics book
 d. in a dictionary

4. What is the meaning of the word *friction* in the note at the end of the passage?
 a. floating
 b. rubbing
 c. slipping
 d. gliding

5. Name two places you could look to find information on kinetic and stored energy.

Short Answer

6. Predict what would happen if the third hill on a roller coaster ride were bigger than the first hill. Explain your answer.

Activity 19

IRA/NCTE
Standard 9

Directions: *Read the passage below, then answer the questions.*

For thousands of years, people throughout the world have used plants to treat illness. Ethnobotanists—scientists who study the plant knowledge of native cultures—have made many discoveries that led to the development of important medicines we use today. In fact, one fourth of all prescription drugs in the United States have plant chemicals as an active ingredient.

In the early 1600s, a European monk saw Native Americans in the Andes Mountains grind the roots, bark, and branches of the cinchonas tree. They used the finely ground powder they called "fever bark" to treat high body temperatures. The fever-reducing ingredient in the plant is called quinine, from the Spanish word *quinaquina.* Today, an artificial form of quinine is used in controlling the recurrence of a disease called malaria.

The commonly used drug, aspirin, came from a plant called queen of the meadow. Many years ago, the roots of the plant were boiled. People drank the "tea" containing salicylic acid as a treatment for fever and pain. Today, we use a synthetic form of aspirin with the same characteristics.

Some cancer medicines were discovered because Native Americans used the rosy periwinkle plant in the treatment of diabetes. When scientists studied the plant to find out whether it was effective against diabetes, they discovered that two of the plant's ingredients kill leukemia cells. Their findings resulted in treatments for leukemia and Hodgkin's disease.

In the mid-1990s, ethnobotanists began looking at a plant used by native healers to treat diseases caused by viruses. The native healers, or shamans, traditionally have been the ones trained to know which plants are good for healing. Ethnobotanists found that the plant used by the shamans contains a chemical called prostratin. Prostratin might stop the growth of the virus that causes acquired immune deficiency syndrome, or AIDS. Some ethnobotanists think shamans could be an important link in the process of turning plants into prescriptions.

Multiple Choice

1. The author thinks ethnobotany is
   a. not effective.
   b. not worthwhile.
   c. only good for curing fevers.
   d. a valuable science.

2. What is the author's main point in this passage?
   a. Aspirin was developed many years ago from a salicylic acid tea.
   b. All plants contain powerful medicines.
   c. Important medicines have come from plants.
   d. Ethnobotanists study the plant knowledge of native cultures.

3. What does the word *shaman* in the last paragraph mean?
   a. a person who looks at plants used by native healers
   b. a person trained to know which plants are good for healing
   c. the bark and branches from the cinchonas tree
   d. the study of native healing

Activity 19 (continued)

4. What did Native Americans use powder from the cinchonas tree for?
   a. to fight diabetes
   b. to cure malaria
   c. to treat fevers
   d. to treat pain

Short Answer

5. Describe how medicines that are used to treat leukemia and Hodgkin's disease were discovered.

   _____

   _____

   _____

   _____

   _____

6. Why do some ethnobotanists believe that shamans could be an important link in the process of turning plants into prescriptions?

   _____

   _____

   _____

   _____

   _____

   _____

Activity 20

IRA/NCTE
Standard 9

Directions: *Read the passage below, then answer the questions.*

Humans have the amazing ability to communicate with each other through language. Human babies can learn any one of thousands of languages. Normally, the first language they learn is the one spoken by their parents. There is good evidence that babies' brains are already programmed to learn language. For example, they are able to notice the difference between sounds at the age of one month. This has been proven with infants from families who speak different languages. In an experiment, these babies could tell the difference between sounds even if the babies' parents never used them. This means that these babies were born with the ability to tell the two sounds apart.

Babies also babble in the same language around the world. It doesn't matter whether they are Ethiopian, Japanese, or American, their early sounds are the same. Between seven and eight months of age, babies start babbling in syllables. They take the sound "ba" and turn it into "ba-ba-ba." The babbling sounds they make are common to most languages.

Children usually begin forming words by their first birthday. Most babies' first words are for objects familiar to them, such as clothes, foods, toys, animals, and people. When children reach the age of two, they use about 270 different words. By the time they are six, they use about 2,600 words.

Although much research is left to be done in the language field, it seems that learning language is a natural function of the brain. As long as a baby is exposed to a language, the baby will learn it.

Multiple Choice

1. What is the main idea of this passage?
   a. All babies make babbling sounds.
   b. Babies around the world sound the same.
   c. Babies are naturally able to learn a language.
   d. Children know about 2,600 words at the age of six.

2. Which of the following statements is NOT presented as a fact in the passage?
   a. Children know about 270 words by the age of two.
   b. All babies can tell differences between words at one month old.
   c. Children start forming words by their first birthday.
   d. Babies start babbling in syllables between seven and eight months old.

3. Which of the following best describes the author's reason for writing this article?
   a. to inform
   b. to entertain
   c. to persuade
   d. to express a personal opinion

Activity 20 (continued)

4. This passage was probably written for
    a. experts in language learning.
    b. people learning to speak Spanish.
    c. students studying the syllables of words.
    d. parents interested in how babies learn language.

Short Answer

5. What proof does the passage give that babies are born with the ability to tell the difference between sounds at the age of one month?

6. How would you summarize this passage? Write your answer in two or three sentences.

Activity 21

IRA/NCTE
Standard 10

Directions: *Read the passage and examine the chart. Then answer the questions.*

Greek and Latin root words often are used in scientific terminology. Some scientific words are the same in English as they originally were in Greek or Latin. For example, the Latin words *species, genera, spectrum, bacillus,* and *coccyx* are still used today in their original form. Other words use Greek or Latin prefixes or suffixes. The chart below lists some commonly used prefixes and suffixes and their meanings.

Latin or Greek prefix	Meaning
a–, an–	lack of, negative
bi–	twice, double
bio–	related to life
bronch–	windpipe
chlor–	green
chrom–	color
endo–	within
exo–	outside
gravi–	heavy
herpe–	reptile
hyper–	excess
hypo–	under
intra–	inside
leuko–	white
micro–	small
macro–	large
neuro–	nerve
ortho–	straight, upright
proto–	first
Latin or Greek suffix	**Meaning**
–derma	skin
–ectomy	to cut out
–emia	blood
–itis	disease or inflammation
–logy	study
–osis	disease

Activity 21 (continued)

**Multiple
Choice**

1. What is a tonsillectomy?
   a. a disease of the tonsils
   b. study of the tonsils
   c. cutting out of the tonsils
   d. an inflammation of the tonsils

2. A disease that affects the skin is called
   a. leukemia.
   b. bronchitis.
   c. dermatitis.
   d. neuritis.

3. The study of reptiles is known as
   a. biology.
   b. neurology.
   c. chromatography.
   d. herpetology.

4. In Greek, the word *therme* means heat. If someone's body heat or temperature was too low, what word could you use to describe this condition?
   a. thermometer
   b. thermotropic
   c. hyperthermia
   d. hypothermia

**Short
Answer**

5. What is the difference between an endoskeleton and an exoskeleton? A microcyte and a macrocyte?

   _____

   _____

   _____

   _____

6. Why do you think scientists rely on Greek and Latin words and names for classification?

   _____

   _____

   _____

   _____

Activity
22

IRA/NCTE

Standard 10

Directions: *Read the passage and examine the sample Web site. Then answer the questions.*

From the Hubble Space Telescope to DNA fingerprinting, science has always been about technology. Computer technology has been a part of the world since the 1950s. The computer revolution led to the evolution of the Internet in the 1990s and now worldwide communication and information exchange is available in almost every business, school, and home in the United States. Scientists use the Internet to gather information, to showcase their work, to find sources of funding for research, and to work with other scientists. The following sample of a Web site illustrates one kind of scientific community on the Internet.

| Home | Search | | About Us | Contact Us |

Welcome to the Scientific Xchange where you can find sources of funding, showcase your work, collaborate with colleagues, and do a whole lot more. Click on any of the links below to get started.

- Discussion Forums
- Funding and Grant Opportunities
- Idea Xchange
- Meetings and Conferences
- Science News Updates

Find a Colleague | Marketplace Catalog | International Partnerships | Security Statement

Activity 22 (continued)

Multiple Choice

1. Which link on the Web site might you visit if you wanted to get a scientific research grant?
   a. Funding and Grant Opportunities
   b. Meetings and Conferences
   c. Idea Xchange
   d. Science News Updates

2. Which keyword(s) would you use to search for information on the increase in Earth's temperature due to the greenhouse effect?
   a. geothermal energy
   b. greenhouse plants
   c. Earth
   d. global warming

3. What information would you NOT find on this Web site?
   a. meetings and conferences
   b. career opportunities
   c. funding and grant opportunities
   d. discussion forums

4. Which link would you use to locate scientists outside the United States?
   a. Find a Colleague
   b. Security Statement
   c. International Partnerships
   d. Discussion Forums

Short Answer

5. What can the Scientific Xchange offer on its Web site that would make it more user friendly for international scientists?

6. Using only the Scientific Xchange Web site, how might you go about compiling a multinational list of scientists who are studying tectonic plate movement?

IRA/NCTE
Standard 11

Directions: *Read the passage and examine the table. Then answer the questions.*

If you've ever been outside on a cold winter day, you know that the wind can make it seem much colder than what the thermometer indicates. This is because the wind is blowing away the layer of warm air that surrounds your body. Also, it is causing the moisture on your skin to evaporate. Both of these actions make you feel colder. It's similar to blowing on hot food to cool it down more quickly.

This phenomenon, called the wind chill factor, can be calculated using the wind speed and the temperature. The wind chill factor not only gives an indication of how uncomfortable outside temperatures are, it also provides a guide to help you avoid frostbite. On a calm day, bare skin can freeze in about 1 h when it is exposed to a temperature of −18°C or less and a wind speed of 16 km/h. At the same temperature with a wind speed of 64 km/h, frostbite can occur in just 10 min.

Look at the table below to see how wind speed affects temperature.

Wind Chill Index						
Temperature °C	**Wind speed (km/h)**					
	8	**16**	**24**	**32**	**40**	**48**
	How it feels					
4	−3	−2	−5	−7	−9	−11
2	−0	−6	−9	−11	−13	−14
−1	−3	−9	−13	−16	−17	−19
−4	−6	−12	−17	−19	−22	−23
−7	−9	−16	−21	−23	−26	−28
−9	−12	−19	−24	−27	−30	−32
−12	−14	−23	−28	−31	−34	−36
−15	−18	−26	−32	−35	−38	−41
−18	−21	−30	−35	−39	−42	−45
−21	−23	−33	−39	−43	−46	−51
−23	−26	−37	−43	−46	−50	−53
−26	−29	−40	−46	−51	−54	−57
−29	−32	−43	−50	−55	−59	−62

Activity 23 (continued)

Multiple Choice

1. Which two variables does the wind chill factor take into account?
   a. wind direction and temperature
   b. temperature and precipitation
   c. wind speed and temperature
   d. precipitation and wind speed

2. If the temperature is -12°C and the wind speed is 16 km/h, what is the wind chill factor?
   a. -23°C
   b. -28°C
   c. -14°C
   d. -19°C

3. If the temperature is -1°C, what would the wind speed have to be to cause frostbite to bare skin in about 1 h?
   a. 16 km/h
   b. 24 km/h
   c. 32 km/h
   d. 40 km/h

4. When does it feel colder?
   a. when the temperature is 4°C and the wind is blowing at 48 km/h
   b. when the temperature is -7°C and the wind is blowing at 8 km/h
   c. when the temperature is -1°C and the wind is blowing at 16 km/h
   d. when the temperature is 2°C and the wind is blowing at 24 km/h

Short Answer

5. Why do you think the wind chill factor table does not include wind speeds above 50 km/h?

   _____

   _____

   _____

6. Suppose you're a member of the school ski club. What would you tell club members about today's ski trip if you discovered that the wind chill factor had reached -18°C?

   _____

   _____

   _____

Activity 24

IRA/NCTE
Standard 11

Directions: *Read the passage below, then complete the writing activity.*

It's not uncommon for different scientists to do similar research on the same topic. For example, scientists in almost every country are trying to find a treatment or cure for the virus that causes AIDS. Scientists often share information and discoveries with each other. It helps them to learn from one another. Write an essay on how working with a partner or in a group can help you with science at school. Be sure to discuss the advantages and disadvantages of learning with a partner or in a group environment, as well as why it's helpful to compare scientific results with others.

_____

_____

_____

_____

_____

_____

_____

_____

_____

_____

_____

_____

_____

_____

_____

_____

_____

_____

_____

_____

_____

_____

Activity 24 (continued)

_____

_____

_____

_____

_____

_____

_____

_____

_____

_____

_____

_____

_____

_____

_____

_____

_____

_____

_____

_____

_____

_____

_____

_____

_____

_____

_____

_____

_____

_____

_____

_____

_____

_____

_____

_____

Activity 25

IRA/NCTE
Standard 12

Directions: *Read the passage below, then answer the questions.*

Animals interact with each other in many different ways. Some animals partner with other animals in a relationship that is beneficial to both. One of the most interesting examples of that kind of a relationship is the one between ants and aphids.

Aphids are small insects that eat the roots, leaves, and stems of plants. They produce a sweet, sticky fluid called honeydew. Honeydew is waste material for aphids, but it is food for ants. Ants, however, do not search for honeydew left behind by aphids. Instead, they keep aphids in their nests.

Honeypot ants live in the southwestern part of the United States. They are one type of ant that keeps aphids in their nests. They "milk" the aphids by stroking them with their antennas. This causes the aphids to secrete the honeydew. Honeypot ants even have workers that store the honeydew in their bellies. The workers consume so much honeydew that they cannot move. Their purpose is to bring up honeydew from their stomachs and give it to the other ants as they need it.

Honeypot ants protect and care for the aphids. They collect food for them and care for their eggs. They protect them from predators like birds and spiders. If the aphids are in danger, the honeypot ants will move them to new nests. They even will move them to underground burrows during the winter.

The aphids also benefit from this relationship. They do not have to search for food, and they are protected from their predators. Because secreting honeydew is a natural process for aphids, they do not have to do any extra work. Living together is advantageous for ants and aphids.

Multiple Choice

1. Which statement is an opinion from the passage?
   a. One of the most interesting examples of that kind of relationship is the one between ants and aphids.
   b. Honeypot ants even have workers that store the honeydew in their bellies.
   c. Aphids are small insects that eat the roots, leaves, and stems of plants.
   d. Some animals form relationships that are beneficial to both.

2. How do ants "milk" aphids?
   a. They squeeze their bodies.
   b. They move them from nest to nest.
   c. They feed them stems, roots, and leaves.
   d. They stroke them with their antennas.

3. The central idea of this passage is that
   a. aphids use ants to find food.
   b. ants use aphids as slaves to produce food.
   c. ants and aphids have a mutually beneficial relationship.
   d. ants and aphids are destructive to each other.

Activity 25 (continued)

4. Which statement below does NOT describe something discussed in this passage?
   a. Ants eat honeydew that aphids produce.
   b. Aphids transmit viruses between plants.
   c. Ants protect their aphids from predators.
   d. Aphids are protected and cared for by ants.

Short Answer

5. Describe a relationship between a person and an animal that would be considered mutually beneficial.

   ....

   ....

   ....

   ....

   ....

6. Summarize this passage for your teacher.

   ....

   ....

   ....

   ....

   ....

   ....

Activity 26

IRA/NCTE
Standard 12

Directions: *Read the passage below, then complete the writing activity that follows.*

In 1996, scientists successfully cloned a sheep they named "Dolly." Clones are organisms that are exact copies of each other. Since the birth of Dolly, people have wondered about the possibility of cloning humans. Eventually, science could make it possible for people to make copies of themselves. Many governments, scientists, and specialists in ethics around the world have started discussing whether or not cloning of human beings should be allowed.

Do you think the cloning of humans is a good idea? Write your opinion and give at least four reasons to support it.

_____

_____

_____

_____

_____

_____

_____

_____

_____

_____

_____

_____

_____

_____

_____

_____

_____

_____

_____

_____

Activity 26 (continued)

Answer Key

Activity 1, page 1
Standard 1
1. a
2. c
3. c
4. d
5. The author believes that the National Park Service had good intentions in prescribing the fire. He or she talks about the advantages of a forest fire. The author blames the wind and hot weather for the rapid spreading of the fire.
6. The author would probably talk more about how the fire destroyed homes and lives and less about the benefits of a forest fire. He or she might place more blame on the National Park Service for setting the fire in the first place.

Activity 2, page 3
Standard 1
1. d
2. b
3. c
4. d
5. Questions might include: Do you live near a mountain?, Do you live on the upwind or downwind side of the mountain?, and What is the weather/climate like where you live?
6. Some students will say a written explanation is most useful, others will say a drawing.Written explanations often provide more detail but drawings can help to simplify an explanation.

Activity 3, page 5
Standard 1
Each journal entry should reflect the writer's state of mind at the time the entry was written. It is likely that the first entry would reveal the writer's excitement and sense of commitment to the cause. The second might reveal a sense of accomplishment and hope that the whale is soon to be returned to the wild. The third most likely would express a sense of disappointment and possibly even anger that Keiko's captivity thwarted attempts to return him to the sea.

Activity 4, page 7
Standard 2
1. a
2. b
3. b
4. a
5. Students who think the Navy was responsible should cite the test results in the June 14 article. Those who think the Navy was not responsible should point to the fact that no direct evidence was ever uncovered to support the assumption that the Navy was at fault.
6. Possible answers: Students should recognize that articles geared toward marine biologists would be written at a higher reading level. They likely would include more scientific terminology, possibly more information about past studies, methods for conducting new studies, and so forth.

Activity 5, page 9
Standard 2
Students should write a clear and concise essay using examples from their own life. The essay should follow correct grammar conventions and include correct spelling, punctuation, and capitalization. Students should elaborate on whether the effects of technology have been positive or negative and explain why.

Activity 6, page 11
Standard 3
1. a
2. a
3. b
4. c
5. Possible answers: Students should recognize that this statement implies

that we have received nothing in return for the money we have invested into space programs. Most will recognize that space travel does have benefits, even if space exploration is a costly endeavor. They should discuss whether those benefits outweigh the costs.

6. Students will need to look at this article through the eyes of an engineer who actually worked on the program. They might conclude that the engineers would be less critical and emotional about their observations of the events that occurred. Students might say that the engineers might point to some of the successes of the overall program and potential for future success. Engineers also could try to justify or further explain some of the errors that occurred.

Activity 7, page 13

Standard 3

1. d
2. b
3. b
4. c
5. Students should include one of the following in their answers: "sun peaking through," "you'll want to carry an umbrella," "temperatures will dip," "expect a beautiful spring day."
6. Students should include one of the following in their answers: "clouds cover much of the rest of the country," "you'll want to carry an umbrella in Cairns," "the overnight temperatures will dip into the 30s."

Activity 8, page 15

Standard 4

1. c
2. b
3. c
4. d
5. Students should indicate whether a written, spoken, or visual message might be most effective in persuading people that tiger poaching is wrong and provide justification for their answers. Many students might choose spoken or visual messages because of their ability to evoke emotion in an audience.

6. The statement is supported by two facts in the first paragraph. The number of South China tigers has dropped from 5,000 to less than 30 in the last 50 years, and worldwide the number of tigers has dropped from 100,000 to between 5,000 and 7,500.

Activity 9, page 17

Standard 4

Students should describe a science tour that they might plan for someone who is just being introduced to science. Their tour should include at least five examples of objects or events in their home or neighborhood that illustrate simple science concepts. They might choose a bicycle or car to illustrate wheels and axles, cement sidewalks or ice cubes to explain changes in states of matter, a baseball game to show action and reaction or gravity, and so forth. Students' writing should indicate that they recognize their audience and purpose.

Activity 10, page 19

Standard 5

1. b
2. a
3. d
4. c
5. Scientists used a laser to measure the height of the glacier at different places. They compared their measurements to those taken in previous years.
6. The author wrote this passage to inform readers about global warming and how it may be affecting Earth. Students should recognize that the last paragraph presents information that could persuade the reader to react because of the fear of possible consequences. Words such as "catastrophic" and "massive flooding" enhance the impact.

Activity 11, page 21

Standard 5

1. b
2. d
3. a
4. c

5. No, the tour is not a good choice for a person in a wheelchair. Since the tour involves extensive hiking and suggests rock-climbing experience, it's probably not wheelchair accessible. The tour is only offered Monday through Saturday from 9 A.M. to 5 P.M.., so going on Sunday at 10 A.M. is not an option. Also, the tour costs $30 per person and is not within the grandfather's budget. Students might suggest calling the tour company to see whether there are any programs available for people who use wheelchairs.

6. Students should select a statement from the brochure that is an opinion and explain that it is based on the author's point of view and not on fact. They should recognize that the brochure, besides providing information, is used to increase the sale of tours.

Activity 12, page 23
Standard 5
Students should write a persuasive letter to their principal, proposing a school recycling program. They should elaborate on the benefits of recycling, as outlined in the article, and present an action plan for school administrators to consider. Students should use accepted letter-writing conventions, including correct spelling, punctuation, and capitalization.

Activity 13, page 25
Standard 10
1. b
2. d
3. a
4. a
5. Students should create two simple sentences from any one sentence in the passage. Example: This process is called irradiation. It kills harmful bacteria and parasites and slows spoilage.
6. Answers will vary. Students should list three topics or details that they would develop further to make this passage into an article; examples: explanation of how the radiation process works; more details about specific food-borne illnesses; types of foods that are most often affected.

Activity 14, page 27
Standard 6
Students should write a narrative-style essay predicting what would happen to them if the volcano erupts again. They should include details about where they would go and what they would do. The essay should contain proper grammar, spelling, capitalization, and punctuation.

Activity 15, page 29
Standard 7
1. c
2. b
3. a
4. a
5. Possible answer: A person tosses a plastic cup into a creek. It flows with the creek into a river and from the river into the bay.
6. Possible answers: Throw trash in garbage cans, not in streams, rivers, or the bay; use fewer pesticides; and properly dispose of chemical containers, such as paint cans.

Activity 16, page 31
Standard 7
Students should write a clear, concise opinion paper stating which disease they believe should get more research money. They should support their opinion with at least three reasons. Their reasons should be detailed and convincing. Writing should incorporate correct grammar, spelling, capitalization, and punctuation.

Activity 17, page 33
Standard 8
Students should compose a set of instructions that outlines, step by step, how to use a microwave oven or other household appliance. They should assume that their audience has never operated the appliance and use their own experiences as a guide. Information should be clearly stated and presented in a logical sequence. The instructions should also include a list of do's and don'ts for using the appliance. In the instance of a microwave, students could list such do's and don'ts as: cover food to avoid splatters, wipe out the microwave after each use, and be cautious when removing foods from the oven, because the container may not feel hot.

Activity 18, page 35
Standard 8
1. a
2. c
3. c
4. b
5. Possible answers include a physics book, a dictionary, an encyclopedia, or the Internet.
6. The roller coaster would probably come to a stop between the second and third hills because it wouldn't have enough kinetic energy to get up the third hill.

Activity 19, page 37
Standard 9
1. d
2. c
3. b
4. c
5. The rosy periwinkle plant was studied to see whether it could be used to treat diabetes. In the process, scientists discovered that it was effective for treating leukemia and Hodgkin's disease.
6. Possible answers: Students should be able to recognize that shamans have a long history of understanding plants as medicine and that ethnobotanists have successfully translated shaman knowledge into medical treatments and cures.

Activity 20, page 39
Standard 9
1. c
2. b
3. a
4. d
5. A scientific experiment showed that babies from families who speak different languages could tell the difference between the same sound. These were sounds that their parents did not use, so the babies must have been born being able to tell them apart.
6. Possible answers: All babies are born with the ability to learn a language. Around the world, all babies make the same sounds and learn the same kinds of first words.

Activity 21, page 41
Standard 10
1. c
2. c
3. d
4. d
5. An endoskeleton is the skeleton or supporting tissue within an animal. An exoskeleton is the outer skeleton or supporting tissue of an animal. A microcyte is a small (red blood) cell and a macrocyte is a large (red blood) cell.
6. Students should recognize the value of having a universal classification system for life-forms and scientific processes. If a different classification system was created in every language it would hamper research, consistency, and communication among scientists.

Activity 22, page 43
Standard 10
1. a
2. d
3. b
4. c
5. It offers different language versions.
6. Possible answers: Post a request in the "Discussion Forums" section; use the site's search capabilities; visit "International Partnerships," or "Find a Colleague," or send an e-mail to the "Contact Us" mailbox requesting help.

Activity 23, page 45
Standard 11
1. c
2. a
3. d
4. a
5. Wind speeds above 40–50 km/h have little additional effect on the wind chill factor. Therefore, they are not included.
6. Possible answers: Students should mention that wind chill factor helps in deciding whether or not it's too dangerous to be participating in outdoor activities. If the wind chill factor falls below -18°C, the club members would be in danger of getting frostbite if they are not well protected.

Activity 24, page 47

Standard 11

Students should write a clear, concise essay that uses correct grammar, punctuation, spelling, and capitalization. Students should list at least two advantages and two disadvantages and elaborate on each. Possible advantages of working in a group include: the ability to check each other's work; more than one person to do the work; or more than one person to think about the data and solve problems. Possible disadvantages include: disagreements between group members; having to explain things to other group members; or having one member slow down the rest of the group. The essay should also include at least one reason why it is helpful to share and compare data from scientific experiments.

Activity 25, page 49

Standard 12

1. a
2. d
3. c
4. b
5. Possible answers: Students might say that people provide food and care to pets, such as dogs and cats, in exchange for companionship. They provide the same for horses, in exchange for work, and cows, in exchange for milk.
6. Ants and aphids benefit from each other. Ants provide food and take care of aphids, while aphids produce honeydew for the ants to eat.

Activity 26, page 51

Standard 12

Students should write a clear, concise essay that uses correct grammar, punctuation, spelling, and capitalization. Students should clearly state their opinion and provide four reasons to support it.